Frontiers of America

MEN ON IRON HORSES
By Edith McCall

The forty some years, between
the time that Peter Cooper built
his Tom Thumb with old gun barrels and other odds and ends
and the driving of the golden
spike in Utah, are filled with
adventurous true stories of the
men who developed the railroads in this country.

Among the chapter headings are:
PETER COOPER'S HORSE & A HALF
THE ARTIST & THE DEWITT CLINTON
STUBBORN HAMIL AND THE JUMP-
ING STICK
WILLIAM OGDEN'S IRON PIONEER
AD CLARK'S RECORD RUN TO THE
PONY EXPRESS
J. MC INTOSH & HIS WAR HORSE
CIRCLING INDIANS & STRAIGHT RAILS
CROCKER'S PETS CARVE A MOUN-
TAIN
LELAND STANFORD HITS THE
GOLDEN SPIKE

Edith McCall brings real people
to life in her stories. And it is the
people who make the history of
any land.

Frontiers of America

MEN ON IRON HORSES

By Edith McCall

Illustrations
By Carol Rogers

Φ CHILDRENS PRESS, INC.

Library of Congress Catalog Card Number: 60-6676

Copyright, 1960, Childrens Press
Printed in the U.S.A.

3 4 5 6 7 8 9 10 11 12 13 14 15 16 17 18 19 20 21 22 23 24 25   R   75 74 73 72 71 70 69 68 67 66

REAL MEN AND EARLY TRAINS

"Mr. Cooper! You need a horse!"

The call came to Mr. Cooper from the open window of a horse-drawn railroad car. The driver of the car had pulled his horse to a stop alongside Mr. Cooper's strange-looking train.

The people in the horsecar were surprised at what they saw. Where a horse should be, there was an open platform on wheels. On the platform, with Mr. Cooper, was a queer machine.

Peter Cooper, dressed as a gentleman of that year of 1830, was too busy to answer. He was dipping water from a barrel into a round boiler that stood on end over a firebox. He checked the workings of the little locomotive that he had made himself. It had iron connecting arms, pipes which once had been gun barrels, a long leather belt, and other odds and ends, which all worked together to make the small locomotive's wheels turn.

Mr. Cooper put another shovelful of coal into the firebox. The calls which came from the horsecar did not bother him at all. Up to now, people in the United States had ridden in something that was pulled by an animal. They would have to be shown what a clanking steam machine could do.

Peter Cooper stood up and wiped the dirt from his hands on an old piece of cloth. He had been getting the *Tom Thumb,* his little one-and-a-half-horsepower locomotive, ready for the thirteen mile trip back to Baltimore, Maryland. His locomotive had just proved, to the men in the open car behind it, that a steam locomotive could be used on the tracks where the horsecar ran from Baltimore to Ellicott's Mills. If a little engine like his could do the work, then surely the gentlemen could see how much better a larger locomotive would be. He put down the cloth, brushed a bit of coal from his coat sleeve, and looked toward the laughing men in the horse-drawn car.

"Good afternoon, gentlemen," he said. He took off his tall hat and bowed. "I have an Iron Horse here, a horse and a half you might say, ready to take my friends back to Baltimore. We shall match your speed or better it."

The driver of the horsecar pulled on the reins to

hold back his fine gray horse.

"We'll wait until you are ready, Mr. Cooper," he said. "Then we shall see which is faster—my live horse or your iron one. Our passengers will see which should be running on these rails!"

That started all the men talking at once.

One in the horsecar yelled, "Hurrah for old Dobbin! Who ever heard of steam pulling a car uphill?"

A man in Mr. Cooper's open car snorted. "Horses are eating up all the money the railroad makes. You don't have to buy oats for an Iron Horse!"

Peter Cooper, waiting for the water in the boiler to get hot enough to make plenty of steam, said nothing. He knew that the new railroad, which had been built for horse-drawn cars, was losing money. He knew that something had to be done or it would be closed. He had a feeling that steam power instead of horse power was the answer. Steam locomotives had been tried in England, and one, the *Stourbridge Lion* had been brought to the United States from England.

It was too bad that the tracks on which the *Stourbridge Lion* had been placed were too weak for

9

it. The heavy locomotive tore up the tracks! But it worked—it pulled along at ten miles per hour.

John Stevens, over in New Jersey, had made a little locomotive for his own use, and it had worked, too.

Peter Cooper knew that his little Iron Horse was not strong or powerful, but people had to be shown that even a small steam locomotive was as good as a live horse, and a strong locomotive would be much better!

"How about it, Peter?" his passengers were calling. "How about a race with the horse?"

Mr. Cooper smiled and said, "We'll see what *Tom Thumb* can do." He was glad that the hard uphill pull was over. The little locomotive had shown that it could pull a load of passengers up the hill, but it had been hard work. People had said it would never make it around the sharp curves, but that had proved quite easy to do. The trip back to Baltimore should be easy.

The men, sitting in the little open car, felt the hot August sun beating down on them and envied the men in the roofed-over horsecar. Peter had a good idea, they were sure, but the heat coming from the fire and from the boiler full of hot water did not make them any more comfortable.

"Are we ready?" one of them called.

Peter tested the steam pressure. He nodded and waved to the driver of the horsecar.

"Ready!" he called. "Go!"

The driver gave his reins a quick shake. The gray horse leaped ahead, pulling his car smoothly along one pair of tracks. The tracks were long pieces of cedar wood, six inches square, topped with a two-inch ribbon of iron to hold the car wheels in place.

"See you later!" the men in the horsecar called back. One put his head out the window to call, "We'll come back for you!"

The live horse got off to a much faster start than the Iron Horse. Little *Tom Thumb* had to get the machinery moving. Starting the train was slow, hard work. The men in the open car felt the jerk of the first push of steam against the piston rod which turned the *Tom Thumb's* wheels. They leaned forward in their eagerness to "help" the little Iron Horse get up speed.

Sparks and cinders flew as the locomotive picked up speed. But the horsecar was far ahead.

"Come on, *Tom Thumb!*" called one of the men. "Show us what you can do!" But he had to quiet down, for the smoke made him cough.

Faster and faster the piston moved. The wheels turned easily, and *Tom Thumb* picked up speed.

The horsecar swayed as it made a turn in the track.

With each turn of the wheels, the *Tom Thumb* was pulling nearer to the gray horse. The next curve found the Iron Horse right behind the live one. *Tom Thumb* rounded the curve easily, pulling the carful of men. In another minute, the locomotive was alongside the horse.

The horse tried to leap away from the puffing, clanking monster beside it. The driver's whip was not needed to make the animal do its very best.

Side by side, the two went down the tracks. Both had to slow down for some of the sharp turns around rocky hill sides.

On and on they went. A long straight stretch was reached. Peter shoveled more coal into the fire-box. He had the steam engine wide open. Now, if ever, was the chance to get ahead of the horse. But he must be careful not to build up so much steam that his homemade boiler with its gun-barrel pipes would burst.

The horse was not used to making the thirteen-mile trip at a full gallop. He began to tire. No matter how sharply the driver cracked his whip, or how loudly the fearful iron monster clanked and hissed and puffed, the horse could not keep up the speed at which he had been running.

Tom Thumb pulled ahead by inches, by feet, and by yards. There was a full train length between the racers, and then several. The men in the open car held onto their tall beaver hats and waved back at the horsecar. *Tom Thumb* had proved he could out-run a horse.

Then suddenly there was a slapping sound, and the engine sighed and stopped.

"What is wrong, Peter?" the men called.

Peter Cooper's face showed his disappointment.

"The blower belt slipped off the wheel," he called. "I'll have it fixed soon, but I'm afraid we've lost our race."

Peter jumped off the platform to put the belt back into place. He was still working at it when the horsecar passed the locomotive.

"Did your Iron Horse break a leg?" someone yelled.

The wild cheers of the men in the horsecar drowned out all other sounds. Peter Cooper, even as he put the belt back into place, was thinking of a way to fix it so that this could not happen again.

"Really, there is no need for me to make the *Tom Thumb* better."

The thought came to him as he climbed back onto the platform. "I have proved my point. I should

leave it to the locomotive makers to build better ones. I am a business man first of all, not an inventor."

The men were quiet as once more the *Tom Thumb* began to move along the tracks. Far ahead, they could see the swaying horsecar and the waving handkerchiefs and hats of the men who rode in it.

"The race is lost, gentlemen," Peter Cooper said, "but steam has won. The Iron Horse will work for less money and do more work than any four-legged horse alive."

When August came again, a year later, Iron Horses were being made ready to pull trains in many of the states along the Atlantic Ocean. The *Tom Thumb* had proved his point.

Up in New York state, a railroad planned just for the Iron Horse had been built from the city of Albany to the city of Schenectady. On August 9, almost everyone in Albany was down at the tracks to see the start of the first passenger train in the state.

"You may take your seats, ladies and gentlemen!" called the "captain" of the little train. He was the man who, a few years later, would be called the "conductor."

The crowd of people pushed toward the little train of cars. But they kept away from the locomotive, the *DeWitt Clinton.*

"I don't trust that thing," one man said. He eyed the tall black smokestack, the boiler with its bouncing valve on the top, the pipes and rods, and the red-hot firebox.

The engineer threw another chunk of wood, taken from the pile on the tender, into the firebox. Then he tested the steam pressure.

"Sh-ooo-sh!" The man who had been looking over the locomotive jumped back so quickly he stepped on the toes of the man behind him.

When he could speak, he said, "I beg your pardon, sir. That locomotive is not to be trusted."

"I quite agree with you, sir. Indeed I do," said the man whose toe had been stepped upon. He stood on one foot and gently rubbed the hurt foot on the back of his leg.

"There is the governor!" someone cried.

The train captain was showing a well-dressed gentleman to a seat in the car behind the tender. That car, and the two behind it, looked like the stagecoaches which were usually pulled by horses.

"Right in here, Your Honor," the captain said. He held open the door in the middle of the side of the car as the governor of New York state climbed in. When each place on the comfortable cushioned seats was taken by one of the important men of Albany, the captain moved on to the second car. Waiting men, all in their best suits and tall hats, were allowed to enter until all three fine coaches were filled. Then the captain pointed out the seats where the coach drivers and others usually sat on the outside of the coaches, at the front and the back.

"A few more of you gentlemen can take these seats," he said. "All others who have tickets will ride in the open cars."

A young man in the crowd quickly folded a piece of paper on which he had been drawing and put it into his pocket. His tall, flat-topped beaver hat had made a good drawing desk, and he had been busy making pictures of the *DeWitt Clinton,* the train that it was about to pull, and the important people who were being seated in the coaches.

"I'd better get on, if I am to have a seat," he thought as he tucked away his drawing materials. William Brown, the artist, got into the line of people who were taking places on the long wooden benches in the three open cars.

He had just squeezed in to a small space between two rather large gentlemen when he heard the captain say, "That is all. No room for any more."

Just then, a lady arose from her seat and walked to the open end of the car to leave it.

"Two places here," she said. "I have changed my mind. John and I will not risk our lives riding in such a thing as this. Come, John."

Her husband, John, got up and followed the lady. He pretended not to hear the laughs of the men he passed as he left the car.

"Too bad, John," said one of the men who hurried to take the places John and his wife had left. "I'll tell you all about it when we get back."

John and his wife joined the many who had come only to see the Iron Horse get into action. Suddenly, many of them pulled out handkerchiefs as they began to cough. A great puff of smoke had come from the *De Witt Clinton's* stack.

"Look out for the sparks!" someone cried. People used their handkerchiefs to brush off the bits of burning wood.

"Stand back," the captain called. He walked to the tender, climbed onto a small seat built at the back of the tender near the top, and carefully seated himself. When he had pulled out his coat tails and settled his tall hat firmly on his head, he looked over the roof of the tender to where the engineer stood waiting on the platform of the *De Witt Clinton.*

"Are we ready?" he asked.

The engineer waved his hand as a signal. The captain nodded and reached down for the long, tin horn which hung from his special seat.

"W-woo-ooooo!" wailed the horn.

"Hisss-sssss!" answered the steam valves.

The engineer pulled on one of the long levers. With a great snort, the *DeWitt Clinton* slowly moved forward. The cheers of the people drowned out the locomotive's noise.

But in a moment, the cheers turned to laughs. The tender and each car was hooked to the car

ahead by a long chain. The *De Witt Clinton* moved
ahead enough to take up the slack in the length of
chain between it and the tender. Then the people
saw the proud captain almost thrown from his seat.
The surprised men in the first coach found themselves thrown to the floor, while the men on the outside seats made quick grabs for the arm rests.

"Governor! Are you hurt?" Men in the first car
were helping the unseated governor back to his
place when down they all went again as the next
car jolted into motion. From then on, it was each
man for himself.

William Brown took a firm grip on the side board of his open car and watched the people alongside the track. Some were doubled up laughing. Others looked most upset. After all, it might not be wise to laugh at the governor, the sheriff and the bank president!

"Uh-hh!" The jolt came to the last car, and William Brown had too much to do from then on to see the faces of the people along the tracks. He and all the others had all they could do to keep their hats on their heads and themselves on the benches.

"Bumpety, bumpety, bumpety!" The wheels were turning faster and faster as the *DeWitt Clinton* put all its strength into the job. From its tall stack smoke poured out in greater clouds as Engineer Matthews threw fresh chunks of dry firewood into the firebox. The flames poked out of the stack, and bits of flaming wood flew back over the cars that followed the Iron Horse.

William Brown was just beginning to enjoy the ride when a tiny bit of burning wood fell on the knee of his trousers. He brushed it off and put it out with his shoe.

"He must have a red-hot fire in there!" Brown

called to the man beside him.

"Eh?" said the man. He pulled an ear trumpet from inside his coat and put it into his ear. Mr. Brown felt foolish yelling into the trumpet.

"The engineer has a red-hot fire under the boiler! Look out for burning bits of wood!" he shouted. But the roar of the wheels, the shouts of people lined along the tracks, and the snorting of the locomotive drowned out his voice.

"Eh?" said the deaf man again. But William Brown did not have to shout again. The deaf man understood when a bit of burning wood fell on his lap.

"Ee-e-e-e-e-ee!" cried one of the ladies. She jumped to her feet to shake a spark from her clothing. Just then, the train reached a turn in the tracks. The lady fell onto the lap of the man who sat across from her.

"Oh, my, my!" she said as he helped her back to her place. "I shall never ride on a train again!"

"Open your umbrella, madam," said the man who sat beside her. "That will keep the sparks from falling on your gown."

A moment later, someone yelled, "Fire! Your

umbrella's on fire, lady!" William Brown reached across and quickly took the flaming umbrella. He threw it overboard just as its flame seemed about to set fire to one of the gentlemen's hats.

In all the open cars, people were having the same trouble. They coughed and choked on the smoke. They leaped up and down brushing off the burning sparks. Those who weren't pushing off sparks from their own clothing were slapping at smoking bits on their neighbor's shoulders.

They were beginning to quiet down a bit when suddenly almost everyone was thrown to the floor again.

"Bump! Bump! Bump!" On it went, down the line of cars. The engineer was pulling hard on the brake lever, and as the speed of the locomotive was cut, each car bumped into the car ahead.

"What is wrong?" William Brown asked as he picked himself up. The train had come to a stop, and the sudden quiet seemed strange.

Up ahead, the captain gave a long, sad call on his tin horn. Then he called out, "Water and wood stop." He pointed his horn toward a wagon, approaching on a crossroad. Barrels of water stood on the wagon box. A pile of wood was stacked near the track.

The passengers climbed from the cars.

"I know exactly what we should do," said one of the men from the coaches. "We shall put an end to that horrible bumping that throws us from our seats."

He walked to the woodpile and chose a strong but not too thick chunk of wood. He soon had the help of other men when they saw what he was doing. He was fitting chunks of wood between the cars so that the slack in the chains was taken up. The wooden braces would help the train get off to a smoother start.

Other men helped load wood on board and refill the water barrel and the boiler. There was plenty of time to finish bracing the cars, for the water in the boiler had to be heated to the boiling point before there was enough steam pressure to start the *DeWitt Clinton* moving.

At last the captain's horn wailed the signal for starting again. The gentlemen, who had taken off their coats while they worked, put them back on.

William Brown looked at the little holes burned

in his coat and at the black streaks.

"I'll never be able to wear this again," he said.

The gentleman nearest him said, "This ride has cost most of us dearly, but it is something we will never forget."

"Nor will we be sorry we went," said Mr. Brown. "It will most certainly go down in history."

"W-woo-ooooo!" wailed the captain's horn. Everyone was ready for the start this time. Helped by the wooden bracing, the *DeWitt Clinton* pulled away to a much smoother start.

The water-wagon driver had turned his wagon about and had settled himself to watch the start of the train. But he had no chance to see it, for at the first snort from the Iron Horse, his live horse gave a frightened whinny, reared, and then plunged forward as fast as his legs could carry him.

Again the little train picked up speed. By this time, the spark-fighting had become a game for the passengers. Their fine clothing was ruined. Since they could do nothing about it, they might as well enjoy the ride. They waved gaily to the people who lined the tracks at each crossroad.

But the people in the buggies and wagons had a

bad time. They had pulled their teams too close to the tracks. When along came the screeching, puffing, roaring monster, every live horse drew back in fright from the iron one. They backed away so quickly that buggies often went over, people and all.

As the train pulled to the end of its trip at Schenectady, the captain blew a warning call on his horn. The sound was lost in the louder roars of the train, but the passengers who saw the captain raise the horn to his lips passed the word along that the train was about to stop.

"Hold tight, everyone!" people cried. They managed to keep their seats even though some of the bracing had fallen out along the way. The waiting people of Schenectady saw a trainload of mussed and tired people pull into their city.

"Hurray! Hurray for the Iron Horse!" someone yelled. The tired people on board the first train in New York state somehow managed to cheer in answer.

After the return trip to Albany, William Brown went to his hotel room. There he took the sharp, pointed scissors and the black paper that were the tools of his work. He was what is called a "silhouette artist." While he could still remember how it all had looked, he set about making black paper cut-outs of the train. His drawings helped him remember where the important people had sat in the front coaches.

When the silhouette was finished, he showed it to some of the people.

"Why, that's the governor!" they said. "And there's the sheriff!"

Through the work of William Brown on that day in August of 1831, people today know just how the train that the *DeWitt Clinton* pulled must have looked.

In the next years, most of the cities in the states near the Atlantic Ocean had at least the start of a railroad. But no rules had been made.

Each railroad chose the size of its locomotive and the distance apart the rails should be set. The train belonging to one railroad could not go on the tracks of another, for it probably would not fit the rails.

Even on each of the little short railroads, rules had not been made. It was enough that the Iron Horse could pull the cars. Soon something would have to be done to make the trains safer.

Each train had two men who considered themselves the "boss." The engineer, who was called the "driver" for a long time, thought that he should be the one in charge of the train. But the conductor, who knew all that was happening in the cars the locomotive pulled, thought he should be the boss. Most people thought so, too, and they called the conductor "captain."

"Captain" Ayres was one of the first conductors

on the Erie Railroad in New York state. He felt that he should be the boss on the train because he knew, more often than the engineer did, when it should be slowed down or stopped. But his engineer was a stubborn man named Hamil, and Mr. Hamil was just as sure that he should be the boss.

One day, something happened that had happened many times before. The iron strap, which was nailed to the top of the wooden rail on which the train ran, suddenly popped up as the train was running along.

"A snake, Captain!" one of the passengers called as he leaned out the window. The curled up end of the iron strap was known as a "snake."

Captain Ayres did not need to be told. He could hear the "snake" as it tore into the under side of a car. The little passenger car swayed and swung and seemed about to leave the tracks.

"Help!" cried a lady. She had fallen from the seat and lay in the aisle, her big skirts keeping her from getting up.

Captain Ayres was yelling to the engineer, "Stop the train!"

But it was no use. He could not make Engineer

Hamil hear. The only answer he got was clanging and banging from the locomotive as it rushed ahead. He turned back to help the lady to her seat.

"I am so sorry, madam," he said. "Are you all right now?"

The lady brushed some bits of dirt from her skirt.

"I believe so. I suppose that if a lady will travel, she must expect such things."

Captain Ayres turned then to see how big a hole had been torn into the wooden floor of the car. He hoped the wheels hadn't been loosened. If one flew off, Engineer Hamil probably would not stop. He would drag them along until they were all killed! Captain Ayres reached for a seat-back to hold onto as the car rounded a curve. He shook his head and sighed.

"I will have to work out a way to signal the engineer," he said. It was not only in times of danger that he needed a signal. Sometimes passengers wanted to get off the train. They became very angry with him when he could not get the engineer to stop.

When the day's run was over, Captain Ayres

walked the length of the train. He looked at each car, at the tender, and at the locomotive. This was a fine new one, made at Mr. Baldwin's new "locomotive works" at Philadelphia. It had a roof over the platform where the engineer stood. As Captain Ayres looked up at Engineer Hamil's working place, an idea came to him.

He turned away and walked to his home in the Hudson River town where he lived. Each day the little train waited until the steamboat had brought goods and people up the river. The people and goods that were going farther west were loaded on board the train, and off it went on its forty-seven mile trip. At each end of the tracks, a turntable had been built. The train was turned about and headed back the same day.

The next morning, Captain Ayres left home early. He took with him a large ball of heavy cord and a hammer. Instead of going directly to the railroad, he headed for the general store.

"Good morning, Sir," he said to the storekeeper. "I have a problem. Will you help me with it?"

"Just tell me what it is, Captain, and I'll do what I can," he said. Captain Ayres took a piece of paper from his pocket and showed the storekeeper what he had in mind. In a moment the storekeeper had gone back to where he kept nails and other hardware. He counted out some U-shaped wires called "staples." They were pointed and sharp at each end.

"Fine," said the captain. He paid for the staples and left the store.

Down at the tracks, there was not yet any sign of Engineer Hamil. Far off down the Hudson River, he heard the steamboat whistle's call.

"I must work fast. That stubborn old Hamil will soon be here," he said aloud. He hurried to the last car and climbed to the roof at the front end.

"Bang, bang, bang!" He had driven a staple firmly into the roof. He went on to the next car and drove a staple near each end of the roof. There was only one more car to go and then the tender. When he reached the locomotive, he drove a last staple into the ceiling of the cab in which Engineer Hamil worked.

He heard the call, "Steamboat landing!" as he worked to run the cord through the staples. He started at the back of the train and worked up to the locomotive. He cut the cord when he had run it through the staple there, and let a few feet hang down.

"One straight piece of firewood will do," he said. From the pile on the tender, he chose the piece he wanted. He tied the end of the cord around it, so that it hung a foot or two down from the cab ceiling.

He jumped down then. He saw Engineer Hamil coming toward the train ready to get the fires going. He watched from a little way off as the engineer climbed onto the locomotive and opened the furnace door.

Hamil stood straight before turning to get firewood.

"Whack!" He banged his head on the hanging piece of wood.

Captain Ayres could hear the engineer swearing as he rubbed his head. Hamil was pulling out the piece of wood as the captain ran forward.

"Who hung a chunk of firewood here for me to run into?" yelled the engineer. "What kind of foolishness is this?"

"I hung it there, and it is not foolishness, Hamil," said Ayres. "It is a signal. You never hear me when I yell, and you never look to see if I'm waving my arms at you. This way, I can let you know when to stop the train."

Hamil shouted. "You mean you can kill me. That will stop the train!"

Ayres said, "I'll hang it lower so that you won't bump your head."

He picked up the chunk of wood from where the engineer had thrown it in his anger. This time he tied it so that it was much nearer the floor. When he had finished, he lifted the cord and then lowered it.

"When you see the piece of firewood jumping like this, stop the train," he said.

Engineer Hamil was about to cut off the wood and throw it out again. But he looked down at the people who had come up from the steamboat landing by this time. He set about his work, his lips tightly drawn.

As Ayres climbed down from the locomotive he heard Hamil say, "I know when to stop this train. No one is going to tell me how to run my locomotive."

He threw a piece of firewood into the firebox

with a bang. Then he connected the leather hose to the boiler to let water run into it. Ayres watched another minute or two and then turned to his own work. The chunk of wood still hung in the locomotive as he showed the steamboat hands where the freight was to go.

Both men were busy until the time to start the train had come. Captain Ayres collected the fares and then blew his horn for the starting signal. The train chugged and snorted and jerked its way ahead.

They were well along on the day's run when Ayres decided to test his signal.

He walked down the aisle of the cars, stopping to warn the passengers.

"The train is going to stop, folks," he said. "Do not think anything is wrong. I have a new signal that I would like to try."

He smiled and waved back to the people as he stepped out onto the open platform at the end of a car. He reached up and pulled a few times at the cord.

"That is strange," he thought. "I can't feel the weight of the piece of wood. The cord seems loose."

He stepped back into the car and held on to

keep from falling. He waited, but there was no sign of the train slowing down.

A passenger sitting near him put his head out the window. He brushed a burning spark from his side whiskers as he pulled his head back in.

"Doesn't look to me as if we are stopping," he said. "Your engineer is putting more wood into the firebox."

Ayres shook his head. "That stubborn old man doesn't know a good idea when he sees it face to face," he said.

When the train stopped at the end of the line, he was not surprised to see that Engineer Hamil had cut the cord.

"Where is that piece of firewood?" Ayres asked.

"In the fire where it belongs," said Hamil.

"Now, look here, Hamil," said Ayres. "That signal is for the good of all the people on the train. It is not just a matter between you and me. Suppose there were a fire in one of the cars. Suppose someone fell off. How could I get you to stop the train?"

Engineer Hamil grunted and turned away.

The next morning, when it was time for the

train to start again, Captain Ayres tied another piece of wood to the cord. Then he turned to Engineer Hamil. His voice was quiet but firm as he spoke.

"If that stick of wood is not on the end of this cord when we get to the end of the line today, we are going to have a fight. One of us will win."

Again, Hamil grunted and turned away.

The train had gone about twenty miles when Captain Ayres tried his signal again. As before, the train went on its way, even faster than before.

"We'll see about this," Ayres said to himself.

When the train pulled to a stop, he helped the passengers out. Then he walked quickly forward to the locomotive.

"Aha! You cut off the stick again!" he said to Hamil. He took off his coat and handed it to one of the passengers who stood near by.

"Get down here, Hamil. Take off your coat. I told you I'd fight you for this."

Hamil turned his back. Ayres jumped onto the platform and pushed the engineer, who had to jump down. Quickly as a cat pouncing on a mouse, Ayres was down on top of him. Hamil was older and

heavier than the conductor. He rolled over, and the fight was on.

"A fight! A fight!" the cry went up. People came running. Soon a crowd gathered around the fighting men.

"Come on, Captain! Give it to him!" they cried. Most of them had no idea what the fight was about. But Captain Ayres was so much more friendly than Engineer Hamil that they were on his side. Ayres was smaller than Hamil, but he could move faster.

Hamil began to puff and grow red in the face. Ayres stepped in with a hard swing to Hamil's jaw, and the big man went down. The conductor sat on his chest and pulled hard on the engineer's collar.

"Will—you—leave—that—wood—on—the—cord?" he asked. Each word was marked with another blow.

"Y-yes! Let me go!" cried the engineer. But Ayres was not yet ready.

"Will you stop the train when you see that stick jumping up and down?" He gave one more blow to Hamil's chest.

"Yes, yes! I will!"

"Will you help me work out some signals, and

pay attention to them?" Ayres asked.

"I said I would. Let me up!"

"Who is the boss of the train from now on?"

Hamil's face was red. His eyes seemed about to pop out as he said, "You are! You are!"

"All right then, Hamil. And if you don't remember this on the way back to the river, I'll teach you the lesson again when we get there."

Ayres got up, took his coat and turned away.

Two men helped the engineer to his feet. He was grumbling as he turned back to the locomotive.

But he had learned his lesson. From then on, he paid attention to signals. The conductor was the boss from then on.

Soon the signalling system was being used on other trains, too, with an iron weight taking the place of the piece of firewood. Later, a bell signal was used, but Captain Ayres' idea of the cord running through the train was used many years.

Eighteen years after the *Tom Thumb* had lost its race, the wind blew hard from over Lake Michigan into the face of a frontier city. The big sailing ship, *Buffalo,* was making its way toward the new pier. On the ship, the sailors worked fast to furl the sails.

A shout went up from the people who watched as the ship came nearer. They saw something big and black strapped on the *Buffalo's* deck.

"The Iron Horse! Here comes Mr. Ogden's Iron Horse!"

Many of them had never seen a locomotive. Even those who had traveled in the East did not know how important this locomotive was to them and to all of the 20,000 people of the city. For the Iron Horse was to make Chicago great.

The shouts of the people on the pier reached the ears of Mr. William B. Ogden as he rode his big horse along the Chicago streets on that October day, 1848.

"The *Buffalo* has come in," he thought. "Watch

that mud-hole, Paddy!" he said to his horse. Paddy stepped around a place where someone had put a sign, "NO BOTTOM—THIS WAY TO CHINA!" A little farther along the block a wagon was sunk too far into the mud for its owner to have it pulled out.

People were hurrying from the frame buildings as the man on the great horse passed them.

"Hello, Mr. Ogden! Has your locomotive come?"

Mr. Ogden smiled and waved and hurried on. The people on foot had to watch each step, for the board sidewalk had a way of sinking into the mud that had followed the fall rains.

Mr. Ogden, hurrying to meet the ship, thought of the troubles he and his partner, Mr. J. Young Scammon, had been having in getting a railroad started. They had gone from town to town, from farmhouse to farmhouse, west of Chicago. At each place they asked for money to help build the railroad. The people in the country were willing to help, for they needed a way to get their goods to market. But in the city itself, people were not much interested.

"Now, Mr. Ogden," some said, "you know that

this year, with the canal open, goods can go from Chicago to New Orleans! Or from New Orleans, goods can come to us! With the lakes to keep us in touch with the East, we don't need a railroad!"

Others said, "If the canal and the lake are not enough, you should spend your time getting more plank roads built. Why, three hundred miles of plank road can be built for the same money as fifty miles of railroad! On plank roads, horses can pull wagons of freight along at ten miles an hour.'

But Mr. Ogden and Mr. Scammon had taken the money they could get and had started the railroad. Now the first few miles of tracks had been laid. Starting just across the Chicago River, they headed west into the rich farm lands. A lake boat had brought the big bundles of strap iron to go on top of the heavy wooden timbers. And now the locomotive had come.

"There should be some cars on that ship, too," Mr. Ogden thought as he hurried Paddy across the sand of the beach. "If there are, the railroad can go into business right away!"

A boy came running toward him as he reached the pier.

"May I take care of your horse, Mr. Ogden?" he asked.

Mr. Ogden pulled Paddy to a stop and climbed down. He gave the reins to the boy and walked out onto the pier. People made way for him as he walked toward the *Buffalo*. He hurried to meet the ship's captain.

"We'll load her onto a barge and take her up the river to the tracks," Mr. Ogden said.

The raw October wind whipped at the people as they watched the unloading of the locomotive. It whipped, too, at the ropes and chains which were slowly lifting the Iron Horse from the *Buffalo's* deck.

A small boy standing near him asked, "Mr. Ogden, what does that word on the side of the locomotive say?"

Mr. Ogden looked at the lettering done in gold, now growing dull, on the Iron Horse's cab.

"It says *PIONEER*, son," he said. "That's her name, and she's a real pioneer, too. She was made in Baldwin's Locomotive Works in Philadelphia twelve years ago, back in 1836. She worked on a railroad in New York state a few years, until they got newer and bigger ones to take her place."

"Bigger ones? The *Pioneer* looks mighty big to me," said the boy.

Mr. Ogden nodded. "She was big when she was built. But in the East, the railroads are doing so much work now that she is too small for them. For us, she will do fine, just as she did in Detroit."

"In Detroit? Did the *Pioneer* run there, too?"

"Yes," said Mr. Ogden. "She was the pioneer locomotive there, too. That is where she got her name. And now she's a Chicago pioneer . . . Easy, boys! Block those wheels so she can't roll on the barge!"

The boy looked at the locomotive that now stood on the deck of the barge. The big back wheels—drivers, Mr. Ogden said they were called — were about as high as he was tall. The *Pioneer* had a great high smokestack, and there were brass bands around its black boiler. A pointed "nose" stuck out from the front wheels.

"What is that pointed thing on the front for?" the boy asked.

Mr. Ogden smiled. "That is the cowcatcher, son," he said. "The first trains had trouble with cows standing on the tracks. The cowcatcher can lift them right off the tracks. Several years before the *Pioneer* was made, someone tried out this idea on a locomotive that came here from England—the *John Bull* was its name."

The boy laughed. "The *John Bull* was a good name for the first engine with a cowcatcher!"

"All ready, Mr. Ogden!" called the men on the barge.

The crowd watched as the *Pioneer* rode into the Chicago River. Many of them followed along on South Water Street to see it reach the tracks which started a few blocks away. Mr. Ogden stayed on to see to the unloading of the six used cars which the *Buffalo* also had brought.

The next day, word spread that the *Pioneer's* fireman, Mr. Dan Sheehan, was getting up steam in the iron horse. He and Mr. John Ebbert, the engineer, were going to take Mr. Ogden, Mr. Scammon, and a few other men on a trial run.

"Stand back, folks!" Mr. Sheehan yelled, after he had worked an hour or so.

Some of the people standing near the *Pioneer* moved back. Those that didn't were sorry.

"Hiss-s-s-s-s-s!" A great burst of steam shot out from the Iron Horse.

"She's ready, John!" Dan called to the engineer. Mr. Ebbert put down his oil can and climbed into the locomotive cab. Two cars and a tender had been hitched behind the *Pioneer*.

Mr. Ogden and the other men who were invited to go on this first ride buttoned their coats to their chins, set their hats more firmly on their heads, and climbed into the cars.

The watching people waved.

"It takes a brave man to trust that thing," said one who was not going. "I'd rather ride a canal boat. This thing might blow up!"

The *Pioneer* shuddered as if to say, "True! But here I go again! I'm old enough to rest, but rest is not for me!"

She let out another great blast of steam, and then settled down to the work of moving the little train along the tracks.

"Chug . . . chug . . . CHUG, chug, chug, chug, chug!"

The men in the two open cars waved at the watching people and then reached for their hats to keep from losing them. Cinders and sparks fell on them, the wind whipped them, and the *Pioneer* did its best to bounce them from the car.

They had just grown used to the feel of the ride when it was over. They reached the end of the tracks.

"How far have we come, Mr. Ogden?" asked one of the gentlemen.

"Five miles," Mr. Ogden replied. "Come and see how the tracks are being laid."

Mr. Ogden showed his guests how the men farthest ahead were building a roadbed of gravel. Behind them, mule teams were pulling heavy six-by six-inch square timbers, nine feet long, putting them where the tie-layers could set them on the roadbed. Every thirty inches, a tie was placed.

Just ahead of where the *Pioneer* stood steaming and sputtering, the rail layers were working. They were spiking long, six-inch square timbers onto the ties in two long wooden ribbons. On top of the heavy rails they nailed oak strips, a little over an inch in thickness and three inches wide. The men who were doing the finishing work were fastening long, thin iron straps on top of the oak strips.

"Very fine, Mr. Ogden," said one of the men who had been invited to come on the *Pioneer's* first trip in Illinois. "I have not thought much of the railroad idea, but perhaps you are right. I have never traveled at such great speed! How fast were we going?"

"At our fastest, I should say about twenty miles to the hour," said Mr. Ogden.

The men gasped. Never before had man traveled so fast on all the frontier!

The *Pioneer* seemed to sigh as steam came from her sides. When the men were on board again, she chugged and pushed her way backward to the city. Her working days had begun once more and, each day from then on, she pulled cars filled with men and the materials they needed to go on with the track building.

Mr. Ogden watched over the work like a mother hen with chicks. When he saw that the tracks were nearly to the DesPlaines River, he decided it was time for a celebration. Work would be slowed down a little at the river until a bridge could be finished.

"We'll invite every man of importance in Chicago for the full ten mile ride," he said to his partner, Mr. Scammon. "They'll soon see that the railroad is better transportation than any canal boat or freight wagon."

The November day of the big opening of the railroad was raw and windy, but almost everyone in town followed the frozen streets to the west end of Lake Street where it reached the South Branch of the Chicago River. They crossed the log bridge and gathered at the place where the tracks began. Workmen were already busy building the first depot in Chicago. It stood near the river's bank, just north of the tracks.

"Can't see why they'll ever need a big building like that," said one of the men who had been invited to ride the train. "Even the business on the canal doesn't need a building that large."

"I agree with you," said the man sitting next to him. "This railroad goes ten miles. What good will it do?" He tried to make himself more comfortable on the wooden bench that ran the length of the little car. Just then he had to take a firm hold on his white beaver hat, for the *Pioneer,* which had been snorting and hissing for some time, suddenly jerked the car forward.

The people watching gave a cheer and waved as the loaded train pulled away. Mr. Ogden had ordered one of the closed cars for people to ride in. When that came, perhaps they, too, would get to ride the train. By now they had learned that they must back away when the *Pioneer* was starting, and most of them stood clear of the sparks that fell from the old wood burner as she moved down the tracks.

On board the train, the men closed their greatcoats against the cold and wind and the falling sparks. Some looked grim. Others, those who believed in the railroad, laughed and enjoyed themselves. They brushed away the sparks and tried not to cough as the smoke blew back at them.

Engineer Ebbert and Fireman Sheehan worked hard to show the important men what the *Pioneer* could do. Faster and faster it rolled along the tracks, past low swampy places and then alongside fields where the rich black soil had been plowed for the winter's rest. To the south, a little way off, could be seen the ruts that marked the rough wagon road over which farmers brought their goods to market. They saw the stagecoach bouncing along it ahead of them.

"We'll pass her in a minute, Dan," Mr. Ebbert called. "Put on some more wood!"

Soon the little train was even with the stage-coach. Another minute and the coach with its team of galloping horses was left behind. Then, almost too soon, the end of the tracks came in sight, and the *Pioneer* had to slow down for the stop.

As the train came to a stop, a man named Charles Walker rose from his seat in the car. He pointed to a slowly moving wagon over on the road.

"Look over there," he called out. "There's a farmer bringing in a load of goods to the city. We'll be back a long time before he gets there with that ox team."

A gleam came into the eye of a man whose name was Beecher. Mr. Beecher had a leather business in Chicago.

"He has hides to sell. See them stacked on top of his load? I have an idea!"

He called out to Mr. Ogden, and in another minute a group of men were hurrying across the prairie.

The surprised farmer heard Mr. Beecher say, "I'll buy your hides, sir. We'll take them back to the city on the train, and they'll be there almost before you can get your oxen headed for home."

Mr. Walker was looking under the hides. The wagon bed was filled with wheat ready for the mills.

"I'll buy your wheat for my mill," he said.

The farmer's surprise at seeing the Iron Horse puffing towards him had been quite enough for one day. Now it seemed the railroad was going to take over the long trip into the city with his goods. He climbed down from the wagon seat and led his oxen over the frozen ground to the railroad track.

The men moved from the second car and crowded into the forward car.

"This will be the freight car for the trip back," said Mr. Ogden. "You gentlemen can find places up ahead, I am sure. And mark my words, this first load of freight is one of many more to come. Freight like this will make Chicago great!"

Mr. Ogden was right.

AD CLARK'S RECORD RUN TO THE PONY EXPRESS

Within three years after the *Pioneer* arrived in Chicago, the Iron Horse was snorting along from Chicago and other cities, toward the Mississippi River. But it had not yet come to the sleepy little river town of Hannibal, Missouri.

One day in November of 1851, a boy named Sam Clemens was working in his brother's newspaper office and print shop. Sam, who would some day be much better known as *Mark Twain*, turned from setting type as his brother spoke.

"Read this over, Sam," said Orion Clemens. "It is my story about the Hannibal and St. Joseph Railroad."

Sam, only sixteen years old, already had a way with words, and Orion often asked his help. The boy picked up the penciled sheets.

"The railroad *can* be built—it *will* be built," he read aloud.

He nodded and, as he put the papers on Orion's desk, he said, "I think you are right, Orion. So far, it has been only speech-making and parades. And some folks say, 'Why build a railroad that starts nowhere and ends nowhere?' But I've heard that you'll soon be able to take a train all the way from the Atlantic Ocean to the Mississippi River."

Orion was putting his story into type.

"Why stop there?" he said. "Hannibal could be as big as St. Louis if a railroad goes west from here."

Just then, the call, "Ste--eam-mbo-oat a-comin'!" drifted into the print shop.

Sam pulled his jacket from a nail on the wall and hurried out into the November air. For now, the railroad was just talk, but the steamboat was real. Sam hurried down to the landing on the river front to see what the incoming boat was bringing.

When Orion Clemens could at last write of the first locomotive to be set upon the partly built tracks of the Hannibal & St. Joseph Railroad, his restless brother Sam had left Hannibal to find adventure. As the tracks reached farther and farther across the wide state of Missouri, young Sam was learning to pilot a big river steamboat.

It was a wintry day in February that the Iron Horse brought a load of people non-stop across Missouri from Hannibal to St. Joseph. Hundreds of people went down to the river front there for the speeches. They watched Colonel W. Broadus Thompson carry a bucket of water down to the Missouri River. The bucket of water had been brought on the train from Hannibal.

Colonel Thompson lifted the bucket high and let the water pour into the Missouri.

"From the Mississippi River," he said, "which is now joined in a new way to the Missouri."

Another bucket was passed to him. This one had in it water from the Illinois River. Then came a bucketful from Lake Michigan.

"Chicago, connected by the iron road as well as by a waterway, now is our sister city," said the colonel. "Goods can go back and forth between us as never before."

Last came a bucket of water which had been brought by train all the way from the Atlantic Ocean. "And most important of all," the colonel said, "St. Joseph is now linked to the Atlantic Ocean and to the greatest cities of the United States."

Cheers drowned out the colonel's last words.

A year later, St. Joseph was getting ready for

another celebration. Families all over the city were talking about the big day that was to come in April.

"They say a Pony Express rider will leave here and ride all the way to California!" a boy said to his father.

The boy's father looked up from a copy of the St. Joseph *Gazette* which he had been reading. "That is not quite right, son. No young man, no matter how strong he is, could ride day and night all week. The young man who leaves here will ride as fast as he can to a 'station' about fifteen miles away. That's about as far as a man can ride full speed without hurting the horse. He'll change horses there. When he has worn out about three horses, he will pass the mail bags along to another rider who will be waiting at a station."

The boy's eyes showed that he was a hundred miles away by that time, out in the open prairie that was west of St. Joseph, across the muddy Missouri River. The father looked down at his paper again. A headline caught his eye.

"Look here, son," he said, "it tells about the plans here in the newspapers. It says that at the same time that a rider starts westward from St. Joseph, another rider will leave San Francisco away out in California. He will head east. In three or four days, a rider coming this way will pass one of them going west."

The boy's eyes were bright. "I'd like to be a Pony Express rider!"

The father smiled. "I suppose it sounds exciting to you, son. But it is the hardest kind of work. It will be dangerous, too. The rider must go on over rough country, riding full speed, no matter what the weather, and day or night. He must also go through many miles of country where the Indians are still trying to hold the land. His life will be in danger."

The boy saw himself riding through Indian country, bent low over his pony as the arrows flew all around him. But his father's next words brought him back to St. Joseph.

"How would you like to go over to Mr. Holliday's stables to see the ponies the freight companies have been buying for the Pony Express?"

The next day, the boy and his father walked to a long, low building. It was marked *Pike's Peak Stable.* Inside were stalls for two hundred horses.

The boy saw fine, strong, young horses that

seemed built for speed. He saw the special saddles that the express riders would use, and the leather "mochila" that would be slipped over the saddle. The "mochila" had four boxlike pockets on it. The mail would be put into these, and the pockets or "cantinas," as they were called, locked. When a rider changed horses, he just took the mochila from the pony he had been riding. It had holes in it so that it would slip over the saddle, and it took only seconds to change from one pony to another. If the pony should fall and the rider have to walk, he would carry the mochila with him.

"I can hardly wait for the day the Pony Express starts," the boy said as he walked back home.

The morning of April 3, 1860, came at last—the day that the boy had been waiting for.

"Everything must go like clockwork," said Alexander Majors, one of the men who had made the plans and paid for the ponies and equipment. He waited in his St. Joseph office for word about the mail trains from the East. The pony leaving St. Joseph was to carry mail coming from New York City, and it was hoped that the fastest time ever made would be on this trip.

But in the newly-opened telegraph office, the word that came clicking in was not good. A messenger hurried over to Mr. Major's office.

"The train from New York was late getting to Detroit. There will be a three hour wait."

Mr. Majors sighed. Everything was ready. Ponies and men were waiting at all the stations, ready to do their part. But the Iron Horse had to do his part, too! The Pony Express rider could not start out from St. Joseph until the train coming from Hannibal could get the mail into his hands.

People were already beginning to come to the railroad station to see the start of the Pony Express when word of the late train came in. The young rider had saddled his pony and ridden down to the station, expecting the train to come in at about five o'clock. Three hours! His start would have to be made in darkness!

People pushed close to the fine looking horse and his fine looking rider. The young man, in his new red shirt, blue trousers, and fancy boots looked ready for anything. But when he found that people were pulling hairs from his pony's mane and tail, he decided to go back to the stable.

Over in Hannibal, a crowd of people was waiting, too. On the tracks of the Hannibal & St. Joseph Railroad stood the locomotive that was to pull the fastest train yet to run. Her fireman had started to get up steam when word came of the late train from Detroit.

Ad Clark, known as the best engineer on the line, had planned to set a new speed record. Now, with the connecting train late, he would have to do better than ever.

He looked over his locomotive with care. She was named the *Missouri*, and had been rubbed and polished until her black sides and brass trim shone like a mirror.

"How fast are you going to travel, Ad?" someone called out.

Ad thought a moment. He had made the two hundred six mile trip to St. Joseph many times. Thirty miles an hour was his usual speed, but that would not be fast enough today!

"Well, sir," he said, "we'll see what the *Missouri* can do. She's a mighty fine locomotive, and today she'll get her chance. My orders are, 'Let her run wild all the way. Set a speed record that will last for fifty years!' "

The track was cleared of all other trains for the day. The switches were spiked in open position for the *Missouri* to go through. Loads of wood and men to put it onto the tender were waiting at the wood stops; water was ready, too. Everything possible was being done to help Ad Clark and the *Missouri* set that record.

Then, at last, the long wait was over. The ferry boat was bringing the mail across the Mississippi River from the puffing train that stood at the end of the tracks on the other side of the river. Quickly, a man waiting on horseback took the mail sack and galloped his horse to the tracks of the Hannibal & St. Joseph.

"All aboard!" came the call. The president of the railroad grasped the mail sack and jumped on board the car where he and other officers of the railroad were to ride.

The *Missouri* puffed out of the station. Hannibal was soon left behind. Then Ad Clark "opened her up" and let the *Missouri* show what she could do. All along the railroad, little towns had sprung up, and people were waiting to see the special train to the Pony Express. But the *Missouri* pulled the train through so fast that the watchers saw little but a flash of black followed by the yellow streak that was the train of cars.

The railroad president had his big watch open.

"A mile a minute! Sixty miles an hour!" he said. Men had never traveled so fast before.

Mile after mile clicked past. The first seventy miles were fairly level, and the railroad bed had been built quite carefully. The *Missouri* was working perfectly, and Ad Clark was sorry to have to cut the speed for the wood stop at Macon.

As the train roared toward the station at Macon, men were waiting there and watching for it.

"Up and at it, men!" yelled the man in charge of getting wood onto the trains. He had built an extra platform, just the height of the tender the *Missouri* would be pulling. As he called out, all of the men he had working for him ran to the wood pile. Each loaded his arms with good dry chunks of cottonwood, and climbed to the platform.

"Scree-ee-eech!" The tracks seemed almost alive as Ad pulled the train to a panting stop in just the right spot for the men to drop the wood into the tender. The engineer wiped his brow and rested a moment. His fireman was loading more chunks of wood into the firebox.

In only fifteen seconds from the moment the train stopped, the men had the tender stacked with all the wood it would hold. At the signal that the work was done, Ad started the *Missouri* on her race again. The men in the passenger car had to hold onto their seats to keep from flying from them as the train almost leaped ahead.

"Hold on, boys!" the president said. "It is a downhill run from here to the Chariton River, and Ad will have us flying!"

Ad was doing his best to make the *Missouri* fly. His hand held the throttle wide-open. Faster and faster the *Missouri* went, streaking fire from her stacks. The fireman threw on chunk after chunk of wood, and it burned almost as fast as it hit the white-hot coals.

The train hit the Chariton River bridge so hard that the bridge shook. Across the train flew, swaying and almost leaving the tracks. The speed took her halfway up the hill on the other side of the river before the *Missouri* slowed down. She puffed her way up the steep hill.

At the top of the hill, the *Missouri* snorted like a thing alive. Like a horse taking the bit into its teeth, she plunged down the other side. Around the curves she swung, and up and down the grades of the roughest part of the trip.

The men in the car behind the tender could not talk. All were too busy holding onto the seats. They knew, too, that they were coming to the part of the roadbed which had been built in a hurry when the railroad was almost finished. The tracks along a fifty mile stretch had been laid on frozen ground, and even a train going at ordinary speed swayed and bounced on that part of the road.

Somehow they held on, and the *Missouri's* wheels did not leave the tracks enough to set her loose. The roar of the train sent cows fleeing as if a horrible monster were after them. The *Missouri* was a fire-spitting demon shrieking through the countryside.

The sun dropped out of sight and the light grew dim. Ad Clark did not stop the *Missouri* to light her lanterns. She was a streak of fire that nothing could stop, save the end of the road.

Then at last, the lighted station at St. Joseph was in sight. With a sudden feeling of lightness, Ad Clark closed the throttle and began to slow down the *Missouri*. The Iron Horse had done her job well. She sighed a great steamy sigh and stood still.

"Make way for the pony!"

Johnny, the wiry young rider, blew on the horn he had slung round his shoulder. His excited pony, feeling the importance of the moment, galloped up to the train, not pulling back from the snorting of his partner, the Iron Horse.

In a moment, the railroad president had passed the important mail packet to the waiting mayor of St. Joseph. The mayor locked the letters into the cantinas. Johnny touched his heels to his pony's sides, and they were off to the ferryboat waiting to take them over the Missouri River. The Pony Express was on its way!

When the excitement was over, Engineer Clark stepped down from the hot locomotive cab. He was worn and dirty, yet he stood like a king while the people cheered and shouted. Everyone wanted to shake the hand that had held the throttle on the record-making run.

The Iron Horse sighed and panted as her partner, the live horse of the Pony Express, reached the Kansas plains across the Missouri River. The live horse, too, would set a record for speed,—a record that would only be broken when the Iron Horse could go the whole way. For now, the job was over. The *Missouri* had done her part, and had done it well.

J. McINTOSH OPENS THE THROTTLE
ON HIS WAR HORSE

The telegraph was clicking out an important message in the little office at St. Joseph. Quickly, the message was re-written on thin paper. It was taken to the Pony Express rider, who carried it for the first part of its trip over plains and mountains to the cities of California.

"Abraham Lincoln elected President!" was the news. Swiftly, the ponies carried the word. They did not have to go all the way to California now, for the new telegraph lines were reaching east from California. When the rider reached a telegraph office, he knew the message would finish the trip much faster than he could carry it.

The Pony Express riders carried two more important news messages before the telegraph wires took over all their work. In March of 1861, the pony boys carried copies of Abraham Lincoln's speech that he made when he became president. The very next month they had bad news to carry.

The first shots had been fired in the War Between the States.

Here and there in the West, men were trying to build more railroads. But the war put a stop to it. The Iron Horse became more important than ever, but for a few years he had to become a war horse.

The Hannibal & St. Joseph Railroad, like the others, carried soldiers from place to place, and brought them the things they needed. Both armies, the "North" and the "South", tried to get and hold each railroad that was near the fighting. The soldiers from the North took the Hannibal & St. Joseph. Each day the *Missouri* and the other locomotives puffed back and forth working for the army.

But little bands of men from the South did not give up. With one of the bands was a young boy of fifteen, whose name was Jesse James. Like the men with whom he fought, Jesse believed he was fighting for what was right. They all did everything they could think of to try to win the railroad for their side.

"Burn the bridges!" some said. "That will stop the trains, and the soldiers and goods will not get through."

Others said, "Why don't we stop the trains by shooting the engineer and the fireman? Then the line will be ours."

Each trip the trains made across the state was a little harder than the one before. Bullets came whizzing in at the engineer and the fireman as they tried to do their work.

"We'll fix that," said the railroad owners. "Bring the locomotives in to the shops at Hannibal. We'll give the Iron Horse a coat of boiler iron to stop the bullets."

Soon there was a great clanging and banging going on in the Hannibal railroad shops. When the Iron Horse came out, he was dressed for war. The men who worked on the trains tried to get ready, too. Each day they met for an hour of practice with rifles, and when they started the day's run with the train, they took guns and bullets with them.

One day, an engineer named James McIntosh was ordered to take a train into St. Joseph. A group of important men were to ride in one of the cars.

Along the way, bullets hit the train once or twice, but there was no real trouble. The trip was almost over, and Engineer McIntosh began to feel less worried.

"Well," he said to his fireman, "it looks as if we'll make it to the end of the line without trouble today. The Platte River is just a few miles ahead, and it is not far to St. Joseph from there."

The fireman looked out through the small window that was left in the cab. At first he thought that all was clear ahead. Then he took a second look.

"Mac," he said as he put his head back inside the cab, "look out on your side. Looks to me like smoke up just about where the Platte River bridge should be."

McIntosh quickly did as his fireman asked.

"Smoke it is," he said. "The enemy must be trying to burn the bridge before we get to it."

He reached out and opened the throttle wider.

"Put on more wood," he said. "Let's keep up full steam."

The fireman stared at him, his mouth open. "Aren't you going to stop?" he asked.

"No, sir. It takes a long time for a fire to weaken a bridge so much that a train can't get over it. If we stop, we're lost. We're taking a chance, full steam ahead!"

The fireman stood a moment as if he wanted to say more. Then he turned to the tender for more wood. As he threw good dry chunks onto the fire, he heard the conductor's signal for the train to stop.

Engineer McIntosh paid no attention to the signal.

"Mac," said the fireman. "The conductor says you should stop. We'll never make it over that burning bridge!"

McIntosh held tighter to the throttle.

"Our only chance is to keep on going. If we stop, you know what will happen to us and to everything on this train."

The fireman looked out the window again. This time he saw more than smoke.

"Mac!" he yelled. "There are men on the tracks! They're waving their arms for you to stop!"

"Let them get out of the way! They can see us coming!" said the engineer.

"McIntosh!" The conductor had made his way over the tender and was pulling himself into the locomotive cab.

"McIntosh! Stop this train!" he yelled. "Can't you see that smoke? The bridge will be out!"

McIntosh knew that the conductor had the right to give orders. But he did not let go his hold on the open throttle.

"Yes, sir. I saw the smoke, and the men on the tracks, too," he said.

"Then stop the train before it is too late!" cried the conductor.

For just a moment, McIntosh's hand moved toward cutting the train's speed. Then he stiffened and pulled back.

"No sir," he said. "If we stop, we are all lost, and all the goods and people on this train will fall into the enemy's hands. We're going to try, anyway."

The conductor took one quick look out the window.

"It's too late now!" he said. "Good luck!"

He turned and made his way back to the passenger cars.

"Down!" he yelled. "On the floor, everybody! And pray!"

Rifle fire hit against the sides of the car. The

men on the car floor felt the sway as the locomotive hit the weakened bridge. They could not see a thing. The cloud of smoke blotted out everything. Rifles cracked outside. The wooden bridge groaned.

The men crouching on the floor of the wooden car were thrown against the seats as the car tipped and swayed. There was a horrible roar, louder than the screaming of wheels on steel, louder than the thunder of the Iron Horse pulling against time.

Then it was over. The frightened men felt the train steady itself on the rails once more. They had

made it over the bridge. One of them pulled himself
to his knees and dared to look out the window. A
curve in the tracks let him see where, only a moment before, the train had been.

"The bridge! It's gone!" he cried. "Thank God
it held!"

When McIntosh put on the brakes for the stop
in the depot at St. Joseph, his hands were still shak-
ing. As soon as the danger was over, he saw how
narrow the line had been between life and death,
not only for himself but for all on the train. If that
bridge had gone a moment sooner! What a load he

had taken on his own shoulders, against the conductor's orders!

As the Iron Horse stood still at last, panting and puffing, McIntosh sat for a moment in the cab. Then he sighed and climbed down. As he turned toward the cars his locomotive had pulled, he saw the president of the Hannibal & St. Joseph Railroad leaving one of them.

"I'm in for it," he thought as he saw the president turn toward him.

McIntosh's face showed his surprise as the railroad president held out his hand.

"You are a brave man, McIntosh," said the president.

McIntosh smiled a weak smile as he shook hands. "No. I am either a hero or a fool," he said. "But no man was more scared than I was when we hit that bridge. I could feel those flames licking at my feet."

The next day, James McIntosh knocked on the door of the president's office. At the call to come in he entered the little room where the president sat behind his big desk.

"Well, McIntosh, good morning!" said the president. "Have you got over yesterday's excitement?"

McIntosh shook his head. "No, sir, I haven't," he said. "That is what I've come to see you about. I'm going to join the army."

The president looked up quickly. "You're going to join the army?" He was silent a moment. Then he said, "Well, I can understand how you feel. A brave fellow like you wants to be in the thick of it. I suppose you want the excitement."

"Oh, no, sir," said McIntosh. "I have to do my part in the war, and I felt I was doing it as an engineer. But it's the excitement I can't take. I've joined the North Missouri Cavalry. I'll feel safer on a live horse than on the Iron Horse until this war is over!"

There came the day at last when the War was over, and the States were united once more. Torn up railroad tracks and burned bridges were rebuilt. The battered old Iron Horse could take off its wartime coat. Then, sides of black and brass shining once more, the Iron Horse could go on with his westward run.

It was the month of April in 1865. General Grenville M. Dodge stood, hat in hand, near the railroad station in the town of Springfield, Illinois. He, with hundreds of other people, heard the sad tolling of the bell of the Iron Horse which was bringing Abraham Lincoln's body home.

"How right that a train should bring him home," General Dodge thought. "Even with all the load of the war on his shoulders, Abraham Lincoln worked to help the railroad building go on. His dream of a railroad all across America *must* come true!"

General Dodge thought of the times he and Mr. Lincoln had planned and talked together of where the railroad might go. That was in the days before the war and before Mr. Lincoln had become President. Grenville Dodge had been trying to find a pass through the mountains where a railroad might be built.

"The Indians do not want to let a railroad come through," he told Mr. Lincoln at their meeting in

1859. "And where we do not have Indian troubles, we are having trouble finding a mountain pass which does not have too steep a climb for a railroad."

Mr. Lincoln nodded. "Never give up, Mr. Dodge," he said. "Our country needs that railroad to the Pacific coast. Nothing is more important to the United States."

Then had come the war years. But even then, Mr. Lincoln had not forgotten about the railroad across the country. He signed a bill in 1862 which made it possible for railroad companies to get the land on which the tracks could be laid. He and Grenville Dodge, who had become General Dodge in the war years, met again to make plans for what they would do when the war was over.

Now the war was over. But President Lincoln had been shot. Grenville Dodge felt that he had lost a great friend.

"And so has the railroad across the nation," he thought.

When General Dodge was ready to leave Springfield, he was asked, "Where do you go from here, General?"

"Back to Indian country. You know, they call me "Long Eye" out there. The Indians watched me at my work as a surveyor and gave me that name. They learned how far I could see through my telescope. I'm going back to go on with President Lincoln's dream of finding a way through the Indian country and the mountains where a railroad can be built—a railroad that will stretch all the way across the West to the Pacific Ocean."

"Where will the railroad start?" asked his friend.

"It will start at Omaha, Nebraska. Going across the plains from there will be simple. But we have to find a mountain pass that is not too steep. Locomotives can't climb a grade of more than about one hundred seventy-five feet of rise to a mile of track. Then, too, the Sioux Indians have to be reckoned with. They do not want to let a railroad come through."

The general's friend said, "It doesn't sound like an easy job to me, General."

"It won't be. I'm sure of that much," the general said. "But many things that are worth while are not easy."

When September came, he and his men were

stationed at Fort Laramie, on the North Platte River in what is now the state of Wyoming. He knew that there were Indians in great numbers to the north and the west—many more than his little army could fight.

"The railroad will have to follow a path farther to the south," he said to his scout, Leon Pallady. "As we go south from the fort, perhaps we can find a pass through the mountains."

Early in the morning, the general and his little army, with a few Pawnee scouts, rode out the gates of the fort and headed south. Three days later, as they were coming near Bear Creek where they planned to camp for the night, Leon Pallady rode his horse alongside the general's.

"General, we are going to run into trouble on this trip," said the scout.

"What makes you think so, Leon? The Sioux, the Arapahoes and the Cheyennes are northwest of here."

"Things have been too quiet," Pallady said.

The general said, "We had better keep it that way. I would like a chance to do some real scouting for the pass for the railroad after we cross Bear

Creek." He looked up at the sky as he felt a sudden gust of wind. "We had better make camp. I don't like the look of that sky!"

Every man set about the work of making camp for the night near the edge of Bear Creek. They tied the horses' front feet together with short lengths of rope. This was called "hobbling," and was done so that the horses could walk but not run. They could not go too far from camp when they were hobbled. When this was done, the men set up their small tents and started chunks of buffalo meat cooking over the fires they built.

Leon Pallady and the Pawnee scouts were restless. Their eyes turned often to the western skyline above the mountains.

"Make those tents tight, boys," Leon said. "The wind is going to hit us hard, and soon."

Fires were put out and the men went into their tents. Quiet came to the camp. But the whinnying of the horses and the wail of the wind through the pines kept most of the men from sleeping soundly.

Leon Pallady closed his eyes but sleep did not come. He could not shake off his feeling that trouble was near. A sudden flapping of the tent canvas brought him to his feet. He went outside and walked quickly to General Dodge's tent.

"General! The storm is coming!" As Leon called, he could feel the sudden coldness of the air in the September night. A whirlpool of chill air tried to lift the little tents from the ground.

"Too late! Stay inside, General, and hold on tight!" yelled Leon, and he crawled back to his own tent. He reached it just in time to save it from being ripped from the ground, pegs and all. All over the camp, men were yelling as they rolled the little tents about them. All they could do was lie on the ground and hold on to the canvas.

Then the yells were drowned in the hard beating of hailstones. There was a moment of quiet in the storm when the sound of the whinnying of frightened horses reached the men's ears. Then the storm hit again.

At last it was over. The men crawled out from their canvas blanket rolls. Water poured down the slopes toward the creek. Hailstones turned to slush beneath the men's feet.

Leon Pallady made his way to the place where the horses had been left. In a minute or two, Gen-

eral Dodge heard him calling, "Every horse is gone, General!"

The general said, "That storm would frighten any horse away. But we'll find them not far away, I'm sure."

But Leon shook his head. "No, General. It would take more than a hailstorm to frighten horses enough for them to break their hobbles. They all ran off in the same direction, too. Look over here." Leon pointed to broken branches, and the prints of horses' hoofs.

"The horses all ran this way. Under cover of the storm, Indians cut the hobbles and frightened our horses away."

The general looked for the signs that Leon's trained eyes had seen so quickly. Then he said, "You may be right, Leon. But why didn't they attack us instead of just frightening our horses?"

"Too many of us for them," said the scout. "It was a small band of Indians, probably a scouting party. But we can be sure they are riding to the camp of their main body right now. Their chief will soon know just where we are and how many men are here."

"Are they driving our horses to their camp?" asked General Dodge.

Leon shook his head "No. I don't think so. We'll find our horses not too far from here. To drive them along would make the going too slow for the Indians and leave a plain trail to their camp."

Leon and the Pawnee scouts set about trailing the horses. The Pawnees felt sure that Leon was right about the Indians who had come in the night. When night came again, all but a few of the animals had been rounded up and hobbled again. The ropes had been cut, not broken.

"Place as many guards tonight as we need to be sure not to be taken by surprise," said the general to one of his officers. Even with the strong guard, the men slept lightly. At dawn, they were ready to move on. No enemy Indian had been seen or heard.

They traveled ten miles that day to Lodge Pole Creek, General Dodge watched the mountain slopes to the west for a place where the railroad might go through, but he saw none.

That night, as campfires burned low, General Dodge thought again of his last meeting with Abraham Lincoln.

"It takes so long. We haven't even found a path for the railroad."

"What did you say, General?" asked the young major sitting near him.

General Dodge blinked his eyes. He had been half asleep, and hadn't known he had spoken aloud.

"The railroad," he said, fully awake this time. "It takes so long to get it started, Major. Tomorrow, we are going to be near a pass I have heard of but have never seen. I believe I will ride the top of the divide to try to see the way through."

The major said, "Have you forgotten about the Indian scouting party?"

General Dodge shook his head. "No. But neither have I forgotten my promise to Abraham Lincoln."

About noon the next day, General Dodge felt sure they must be near the pass of which he had heard. He called for twelve men who were willing to go to the top of the ridge with him. If Indians came to attack, each of the men would stand out against the sky as a target. But more than twelve were willing to go. The rest of the army was to follow along at the foot of the hills as far as Crow Creek.

General Dodge and Leon Pallady led the way. They rode their horses to the top of the ridge. From there they could see for many miles across valleys and ridges to more high mountains beyond. Below them, to the left and back a way, they could see the slower-moving army making its way toward Crow Creek.

It was about four o'clock in the afternoon when Leon Pallady suddenly pulled his horse to a stop and called to the general. General Dodge had been studying the land to the west through his telescope. He folded it and put it into its case. So far, he had not been able to see how a railroad could get through. Yet he knew the pass must be near.

"General!" Leon's call brought General Dodge riding to his side. Leon pointed down the bank to the woods just above the path the army would soon be following.

"Indians!" he said.

General Dodge pulled out his telescope again.

"Crows!" he said. "And many of them!"

He handed the telescope to Leon. The scout

could see the Indians clearly.

"It's a war party," he said. "I reckon there are about three hundred of them."

"Do they see us?" asked the general.

"They've been following us all day. They will close in on us when we camp for the night."

General Dodge looked back at his twelve picked men on horseback. Good soldiers as they were, they were no match for three hundred Crows on the warpath.

Leon gave the telescope back to General Dodge. Somehow, the little party would have to get to the main army. Probably the main army had not seen the war party, for the trees on the mountain slope gave them cover.

He said to the general, "If we try to get to the army by riding ahead and downward and circling back, they will know what we are trying to do. They will attack. If we start down and head back to the army, we walk into their arms. What do you think we had better do, General?"

The general and his scout had kept their horses heading onward, as if they had not seen the Indians below and behind them. The rest of the men knew something had been seen down the slope, but they were good soldiers and went on as if nothing were wrong.

General Dodge said, "If there is some way we can signal the army to attack from below—"

"Smoke signals!" said Leon. "We will have to work fast, but we will use the Indians' own game."

The two rode on as they worked out their plan. At last they saw the right spot to carry it out. They had rounded a turn that took them out of sight of the Indians for a few minutes. The general passed the word to the twelve men to ride down from the ridge to a patch of woods. There they were to get down from their horses and run on foot into the woods.

Each man checked his rifle and his ammunition. A fight was sure to come. But if they could get the attention of the Indians, the army would have a chance to ride into battle.

Quickly they followed their plan, leaving the horses just above the wood and hurrying to get the signal fire started before the Crows should find out what they were doing. The shadows were darkening the woods on the east slope of the mountain. That would help them in their plan for the signals would be seen more quickly.

Soon pine boughs and dry leaves were crackling. As the heat of the spreading fire drove the men back to hiding places behind rocks, they heard the shouts of the Crows.

"The army can't help but know what is wrong," General Dodge said as he took a place not far from Leon. He called out an order to the men to hold their fire until the Crows were very near. "Our rifles have a longer range than theirs, I am sure," he said. "When I fire, act quickly, for they will hurry in to get close enough for their rifle shots to reach us."

Leon's trained eyes caught the low rush of brown as the Indians moved from rock to rock, coming nearer every moment.

"There, General," he said softly. General Dodge was quick to open fire. An awful cry came from the Indian at whom he aimed. The hurt man ran closer for a moment, and then fell forward onto the ground.

The battle was on. Each man was kept busy firing and reloading from that moment.

"We can't hold on for long," the general thought. "If only the army comes in behind the Indians before we run out of ammunition!"

There was no time to look through the telescope to see if help was coming. There was no time for anything but to fire at any Indian who showed himself, to fire and to reload. By this time, the Indians were taking cover behind the rocks that were left as the woods burned.

General Dodge prayed for time—time before darkness set in, darkness that would give cover to three hundred Indians who could circle them with no trouble. Fourteen men alone on a mountain side would have no chance!

Then, faintly at first, came the shouts of the men of Dodge's army as they rode into battle and the yells of the Crow Indians. The direction of battle turned.

"Circle low and charge!" cried Dodge. "Get your horses and ride as you never rode before!"

The men, freed from the charge of rifle fire, hurried to their horses. As they reached the higher ground where they had left them, they looked down and saw the army charging up the mountain side. And above them, Crow Indians on their tough ponies, were riding upward and away. They did not

want a battle for which they were not ready!

Indian ponies began to show as black shapes against the evening sky. Over the ridge their riders hurried them, and quickly they dropped downward on the other side of the mountain.

General Dodge turned his horse toward the ridge, too. As he rode upward, he saw the last of the Indian ponies disappear. He reached the top and pulled his telescope from its case. Then "Long Eye" watched the Indian band in its flight.

"They'll break their ponies' legs riding down the slope so fast!" he thought.

But the Indians knew what they were doing. The path they followed did not drop nearly so fast as it seemed to from above. The way they followed, as they swung off into a valley, was not steep at all.

"Leon!" he called to his scout. "Come here!"

When Pallady was beside him, General Dodge pointed out the way that the Indians had gone.

"That's it!" said the general. "The Indians have shown us the way. Through that valley some day, the Iron Horse will follow where the Indian ponies led us."

The general's troubles were not over, but he did not forget the place where he had almost lost his life that September day in 1865. The day was to come when graders and track layers would come to that same spot, marking the way for the Iron Horse.

STRAIGHT RAILS AND CIRCLING INDIANS

At last the big hammers were ringing out against the spikes. Rails were going down on the prairie west of Omaha, Nebraska. The Union Pacific, a part of Abraham Lincoln's great dream, was really started.

Out in California, work had begun on the Central Pacific Railroad. But out there, the mountains stood ready to slow down the work.

"The Union Pacific will lay many more miles of track than the Central Pacific," General Dodge told the men who were helping pay for the railroad. "We should be able to lay three or four miles of track across the plains every working day."

And that is what the men were doing. Out in the Nebraska countryside, it looked as if an army had made camp. Near Fort Kearney, big wooden buildings had been put up in which the workmen could sleep. There was a tent, forty feet wide and a hundred feet long, where a brass band played dance music in the evenings. When the railroad had gone too far the other side of Fort Kearney, the "town" of light wooden buildings and tents would be picked up and moved on.

Every day an army of men set off to work. The men were soldiers in need of work now that the War Between the States was over. They were men too restless to stay at home in the towns in the East. And many of them were men who had come to the United States from Ireland, looking for work.

"We have one thousand men, and can use every one of them," Dan Casement told General Dodge. He and his brother, John Casement, had been chosen to "boss" the work of track-laying.

"One thousand men, and one hundred strong teams of mules and oxen," John added. "And they are putting their hearts into the work as if they were fighting a war."

How much of a "war" it was to be, even the Casement brothers did not know.

By August of 1866, they began to find out. The surveyors, marking the line the tracks would follow, were far ahead, almost to the western edge of Nebraska. Behind them came the graders, smoothing off the land with heavy "drags" pulled by ox or mule teams, and shoveling out the high places and filling in the low ones.

Heavy wagons brought the gravel and the ties that went down when the grading was done. Train-loads of steel rails came to St. Joseph, Missouri. There they were loaded onto steamboats and taken up the Missouri River to Omaha. And as the rails went down, a work train followed close behind. The work train carried each day's supplies to the end of the tracks.

One August day, General Dodge's special car had been pulled two hundred miles west from Omaha before it reached the end of the tracks.

The General walked ahead to where the strong, sun-browned workmen were pounding the big spikes that held the rails in place. He was watching the sure way in which one of the men brought down the heavy hammer when he heard the fast beat of horses' hoofs.

He turned and saw a rider coming towards him. The man was excited.

"General Dodge! General Dodge!" he called. "Indians! They've got the freight train!"

"Indians already? We aren't into Indian country yet!"

"They're setting it on fire, General. They rode up, yelling and screaming that wild way, and stopped the train!"

The man waved his arms and screamed himself in his excitement. The general did not wait to ask him more. He hurried to the work train locomotive. It had brought General Dodge's private car and several open flatcars of ties and rails out to the end of the line, backing them from the last siding. Now the locomotive stood headed east, with General Dodge's car hooked behind the tender.

The engineer and fireman were cleaning and oiling the old locomotive as General Dodge hurried up to them.

"Get up steam, boys! Indians have attacked the freight train!"

The fireman jumped to the locomotive cab. He opened the firebox door and began raking out the ash bed. He threw in kindling wood, and as soon as it was burning, put in chunks of dry cottonwood.

"How far up the track, General?" he called down.

General Dodge turned to the rider. "Where is the train?" he asked.

"Back at Plum Creek—ten miles or so," said the rider. He was hot after his fast ride, and wiped his face with his sleeve. The back of his shirt was wet.

"We'll be on our way soon," said the general. "No Indian party is going to stop this railroad from being built!"

He turned and hurried back to the men who were working on the tracks.

"I need twenty men!" he called. "Twenty men willing to fight the Indians—" More than twenty men dropped their tools and stepped forward. Mostly Irishmen, they were, and the day that held excitement of a fight was a good day to them.

"Come on, then!" called the general. He ran to the back end of his private car.

"Pull the pin on that coupling!" he called. He pointed to the iron pieces that held the flatcar to his car.

"Have you got rifles?" one of the men asked.

The general signalled for the men to get into the car.

"Everything is here that we need," he said. "I

had this car fitted out for times such as this."

The car into which the men climbed had been a plain passenger car, with wooden sides and straight-back seats. But General Dodge had had iron plates put all over its sides. Inside, there were racks which held rifles and ammunition. The general knew that bands of Indians would fight the railroad all the way across the West. He was as ready as he could be.

"All aboard!" he called to the engineer.

Great puffs of smoke came pouring from the big stack of the Iron Horse. With the light load it pulled, it leaped ahead, faster with each puff. Soon it was flying eastward along the shiny new rails.

In the general's car, the men were checking the rifles and getting them loaded. The general gave each man a place from which to fire. Then there was nothing to do but wait and watch.

They had been on the way about ten minutes when one of the men saw smoke ahead.

"There she is, General!" he called.

General Dodge stepped out onto the open platform at the front of the car. He leaned out until he could see what was ahead. There stood the train, smoke and flames coming up from the much needed loads of freight. Indians were circling the train on their fast ponies. They fired into the cars as they rode by.

The locomotive pulled up, nose to nose, with the freight engine. General Dodge stepped quickly back inside the car. With a steamy shudder, the old work engine stood still.

There was no room, now, for the Indians to cut in front of the freight train. Their circle had to go around the work locomotive, its tender, and the general's car, too.

"Bang! Bang! Bang!"

From each window of the iron-plated car, a rifle nosed out. From each rifle, a bullet flew out at the yelling Indians.

Only once did the Indians try to circle the car from which the rifles reached out with their deadly fire. Those that lived through the first trip rode away to the north and the west.

"Well done, men," said General Dodge. "This is something we can expect to do often as the railroad goes farther west. Now let's go see what we can do for the freight and the men on the train."

With the Indians gone and the waters of Plum Creek near by, the fires were soon put out. The crew of the freight train could come up from the floor of the locomotive cab and tender where they had been hiding. None of the trainmen had been hurt.

Indian fighting became part of the work of building the railroad. Even the hunters who went out each day to get buffalo meat to feed the hungry workmen often had to ride for their lives.

CROCKER'S PETS CARVE A MOUNTAIN

While General Dodge and the Casement brothers moved the Iron Horse farther and farther to the west, other men were fighting to get tracks laid in California. The Central Pacific Railroad started there, and was to go east until it met the Union Pacific.

Indians did not block the way for the Central Pacific, but mountains of rock did. Almost as soon as the grading began, rock had to be chopped and blown away.

Tunnels were the answer, sometimes. Foot by foot, a hole was cut through a mountain when there was no way to go around it. When the floor of the tunnel was flat enough, tracks were laid. Then the locomotive *Governor Stanford* could nose its way in with more loads of rails and ties. The *Governor Stanford* had been brought to California by sailing ship, all the way around the southern end of South America.

Once, Charlie Crocker, who was in charge of the

work, was determined to get around a mountain. But the side of the mountain went almost straight down. At the bottom was the American River.

"Well, Charlie," said Mr. Montague, the chief engineer, "there is only one way. We will have to chop a shelf on the mountain side. And the only way to do that is to lower men in baskets from the top of the cliff. "

"You're joking," said Charlie.

But he went to the top of the cliff and looked over the edge.

"That's how we'll do it," he said.

When the ropes and chains and baskets were up there, he asked for men who were willing to hang on the mountain side to work. His answers of "I will" came in Chinese.

The graders for the Central Pacific were almost all Chinese. Thousands of them had come across the Pacific Ocean to work, and work they did! Anything Charlie Crocker wanted from them, they gave. "Charlie Crocker's Pets," they were called. Those who watched how hard they worked could see why.

In those days, the Chinese men wore their hair in long braids which hung down their backs. They

jammed their blue caps on their heads, grinned, and with long braids flying, set to work. Into the baskets they went, and down the mountain side. Their picks dug into the cliff, and soon rock was falling to the river below.

All summer, the men worked day and night. Bonfires and candles lighted their work when darkness came. They knew that when winter came, snow would block the work in the mountains. Even in June, twelve feet of snow covered one new section of track.

"Put a roof over it," said Charlie. After that, for forty miles, the locomotives ran under a roof that kept the snow off the tracks.

General Dodge sent some Union Pacific men to California to see how Charlie Crocker's Pets were doing.

"It will take them years to get through those mountains" they told the general.

"Where do you think the lines will meet?" the general was asked.

"We may reach the California line before the Central Pacific does. That means more government money for us. We are lucky fellows, at that!"

But General Dodge did not know the fight that was in the Central Pacific men.

"Let's show 'em," Crocker would say, and the "thing that couldn't be done" would get done.

There was the job of moving the *Black Goose,* for one thing. The *Black Goose* was a great steam engine that could be used for lifting and moving heavy loads. It was needed for work on the highest tunnel of all.

"The *Black Goose* can do the job," said Mr. Montague. "But, Charlie, how are we going to get that big heavy machine moved to the tunnel? If we wait until the tracks get that far, there will be weeks when our track layers cannot work. Cutting a tunnel takes a long time."

Charlie Crocker ran his hand through his long beard. Then he turned to Montague with that "we can do it" look in his eye.

"We'll get Missouri Bill. He can do it."

Missouri Bill was a giant of a man, bigger than Charlie Crocker himself. He was what they called a "bullwhacker." He could make a team of mules or oxen work as they had never worked before.

All the parts that could be taken off the *Black*

Goose were sent on ahead. Then the monster of a machine was put on a flatcar. The Iron Horse pulled it to the end of the tracks.

"Here the job begins," said Missouri Bill. He and all the other strong men that could be found worked to get the engine off the flatcar and onto a set of jacks. With the jacks, they moved it a few inches at a time until they got it onto a logging wagon. The logging wagon had wheels two feet wide to keep it from sinking into the mud.

"Bolt her down tight!" called Missouri Bill as he hitched up his twenty ox team.

"That's a lot of animal for one man to handle," Mr. Montague said to Charlie.

"No one but Bill could do it," said Charlie. "We'll send other men along on foot to help in case of trouble."

Then Missouri Bill began to talk to his oxen. Gently at first, and then louder. He took the reins, and a stream of words meant only for the oxen's ears rang out. It ended with a sudden loud yell. The long whip sang out over the oxen's heads. Like one great animal, they all pulled together and the *Black Goose's* ride up the mountains began.

Steadily they moved along. All went well until a ten mule team came toward them along the narrow mountain trail. The mules were pulling a load from one of the mines.

"Whoa! Whoa!" yelled the mule driver. But all the "whoas" would not stop his mules when they heard and saw the black monster coming toward them. They broke harness and left the trail. Their driver's words are said to have "burned the bark off the trees!"

Next to come towards the monster was a stage-coach.

"Whoa! Whoa!" shouted the driver as he pulled on the reins. But again the team could not be held.

"Bill!" called one of the men. "I'll ride ahead to meet the next teams. I have an idea that I think will work."

He did as he said, and the next team that came toward the *Black Goose* wore blindfolds. They could not see as they were led past the engine. Even so, they trembled with fear at the clanking and banging.

When at last the *Black Goose* was set in place to do its work, Missouri Bill fed his oxen and himself well, and all could rest. It had taken six weeks to haul the *Black Goose* up the mountains!

Work on the Pacific Railroad had been going on for almost three years when a Central Pacific Iron Horse poked its nose across the California-Nevada line. General Dodge could hardly believe it when he heard that the mountains had been crossed.

Then the race was on. Each railroad knew that the end was in sight. Each wanted to get as many miles laid as possible.

"Let's see what we can do in one day," the Casement brothers said to their men. It was early spring of 1869, and the Union Pacific was working in Utah as the Central Pacific men laid track across Nevada. Three miles was the usual length of track laid in one day's time.

The Union Pacific's men tried very hard one day to see what they could do. They laid six miles between dawn and dark.

"Wait until Central Pacific hears about that!" said General Dodge. "They'll turn green!"

"Or blue," said someone. "They'll feel so bad!"

"Or red," said another, "because they'll be so mad!"

But the Union Pacific men forgot what fighters the Central Pacific men were.

"Let's show 'em" said Charlie Crocker when he heard about the six miles of track in a day. He even invited General Dodge to come to see how many miles his men could lay in a day's time.

Charlie Crocker's "pets" were off before daylight, grading as they had never graded before. Behind them were two thousand Americans, with ties and spikes and rails. Before the sun was all the way up that April morning, they had laid two miles of track.

Loads of ties and rails were dumped right where they were needed. Men stood ready to keep everything moving. The rails went down as fast as they were brought to the track's end. Two hundred forty feet of rail went down in one minute and fifteen seconds.

When the sun went down and darkness came, ten miles and fifty-six feet of track had been put in place and was ready for the Iron Horse!

"You win this time," said General Dodge. He went back to his Irishmen whose job was nearly finished. Already the surveyors and graders had met and passed each other. Word must soon come as to where the two sets of tracks were to meet.

Then the message came from Washington, "Promontory, Utah, first week in May."

That first week of May in 1869, people came to the little frontier town of Promontory, Utah, to see the meeting of the two railroads. They could see nothing but little shacks dripping with rain, on a street that was more mudhole than anything else. Someone tried to brighten up the buildings with strips of red, white and blue cloth. But more rain came, and even snow. The town looked sadder than ever in its wind-torn, rain-soaked decorations.

The track-laying had been finished on May 2. The Casement brothers' Irishmen, and Charlie Crocker's Chinese walked about the little town with nothing to do. Everything was ready for the driving of the last spike—the golden one that would mark the opening of the railroad all the way across the United States.

"Four years of fighting Indians, walls of rock, tons of snow, and now rain!" said the waiting people. Four years. But it had been almost forty years since Peter Cooper raced the horsecar.

"They say the floods are so bad that the train from the east can't get through!"

Charlie Crocker's railroad officers got to Promontory on Friday, May 7, in a special train from California. Telegraph lines brought word that the Union Pacific train could not come through the flooded country to the east until the rain let up.

Charlie and Engineer Montague talked things over.

Mr. Montague said, "This town of Promontory will be important for freight shipping. We've seen it happen all along the tracks. Where a new town was started or an old one was already, the coming of the railroad made business grow fast in the town. Now, Charlie, while we are waiting, I think we should use our men to build a siding here."

Charlie nodded. "If we don't, Union Pacific will. Let's say nothing about it, but the first day the rain stops, we'll be ready to go to work."

A work train was made up about one hundred miles west of Promontory. It was loaded with men and all the things they would need to build the extra track. Saturday the rain slowed, and by evening it had stopped.

"Be ready to build the siding, starting early to-morrow morning, boys," said Charlie.

At dawn, the Central Pacific work train pulled into Promontory.

"Charlie!" yelled Montague. "What is this?"

The two men stared at a brand new set of rail-road siding tracks, all laid, just as they had planned to do on that day. One of the Casement brothers heard the yell.

"We beat you to it this time," he said. "Our Union Pacific boys worked all through the night. We win, this time!"

All that day, the hopes grew that on Monday the Union Pacific train would be able to come through. The weather turned colder and windier. There were a few snow flurries, and an icy wind swept through Promontory and along the railroad tracks. It wasn't pleasant, but it began to dry up the mud.

"This is the day!"

Word passed quickly on Monday morning, May 10. The telegraph operator in Promontory stayed close to his receiver until word came that the Union Pacific train was really coming through.

Then he began to get ready for what was to be the first report of an important happening *while it was happening*. All over the United States, telegraph operators would be at their stations waiting for the clicks that would come over their wires from Promontory, Utah. He himself would be busy tapping out the messages that told what was happening at the celebration.

One very special arrangement was made. When Governor Leland Stanford of California actually hit the gold spike, the operator would not tap out the message. Instead, there were wires hooked to the big silver hammer and to the spike. The blow of the hammer on the spike would be heard as a "click" on the wires. Nothing like this had ever been done before, for the telegraph lines had not been finished much ahead of the railroad itself.

Morning passed. The crowd grew restless. A camera that was set up was interesting for the people to see, for many of them had never seen one of those boxes that could make pictures. They looked at the telegraph operator's table and asked him many questions. But time passed slowly.

At noon, everyone in Promontory who had food

to sell did a good business. Another hour went by.
Feet began to hurt, and people were cold, for the
wind took the warmth out of the May sunshine.
The men of the Camp Douglas Band arrived in
their blue uniforms. They played a few marches, but
even that did not help much.

Then at last the far-off wail of the Iron Horse
was heard coming from the east. People rushed to
get the good places they had left. The big celebration was about to begin.

The cheers and band music almost drowned out

the last steamy sighs of the Union Pacific's coal-burning *No. 119*. But all eyes were upon the long awaited Iron Horse as it pulled up and stopped a few feet from the cowcatcher of the Central Pacific's wood-burning *Jupiter*.

There was no time to be wasted. The celebration must be over before darkness came. The telegraph operator took his place.

"The driving of the spikes is about to begin," he tapped out. "First spike is a silver one from Nevada. When the speech is made, it will be driven into place with a silver hammer."

"The silver spike is driven," he tapped a little later.

When another speech had been made, he reported the driving of a spike from Arizona. This one was made of iron covered with silver, except for its top of gold. Then there were more speeches, and spikes from Idaho and Montana. Each spike was driven into a hole that had been drilled for it in the polished wooden tie.

Then came the most important part of all. The telegraph operator got up from his table, to check the wires on the big silver hammer and the last and most important spike — the golden one from California.

The last speech was made, and Governor Stanford picked up the hammer with the wires attached. Up it went, and down it came. But the governor had waited too long and was tired. He missed the spike.

Quickly the telegraph operator tapped with his key, so that the world would hear the signal. For this was the tap that was to start a celebration all over the United States. At that instant, in many cities fire bells rang, whistles blew, and people shouted.

The Atlantic and Pacific Oceans were joined by rail!

At Promontory, the two locomotives stood facing each other. The firemen and engineers were ready. Slowly each inched forward until they stood nose to nose, touching each other.

The telegraph operator tapped out his closing message.

The last rail is laid.

The last spike is driven.

The Pacific Railroad is finished.

It was finished, but it was only a beginning. Abraham Lincoln's dream of a nation whose cities were joined by rails was coming true faster than even he had thought it would. For while the Pacific Railroad was being built, other tracks were being laid, too. A criss-cross of rails was tying city to city, state to state.

Everywhere the Iron Horse went, business grew, for it could pull the goods to market, faster and better. The United States was truly "united" at last, because of the MEN ON IRON HORSES.

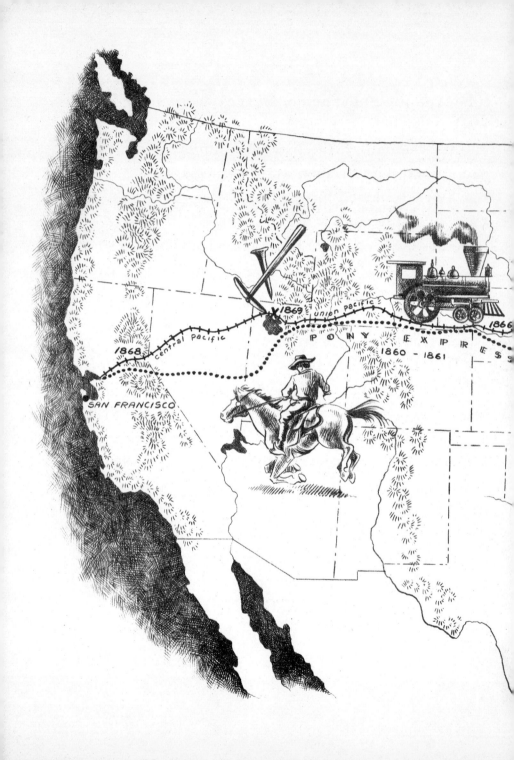

1869 union pacific 1866

1868 central pacific

SAN FRANCISCO

PONY EXPRESS 1860 - 1861